Be kind, be brave and
be polite ...
Mumma's words were
spoken each night.
Read a book every
day, are the words
that she would say.

Be kind, be brave and
be polite,
Mumma's words were
spoken each night.
Look in the mirror and
love what you see,
individuality.

Be kind, be brave and
be polite,
Mumma's words were
spoken each night.
Love our planet she would
say, we must protect it
night and day.

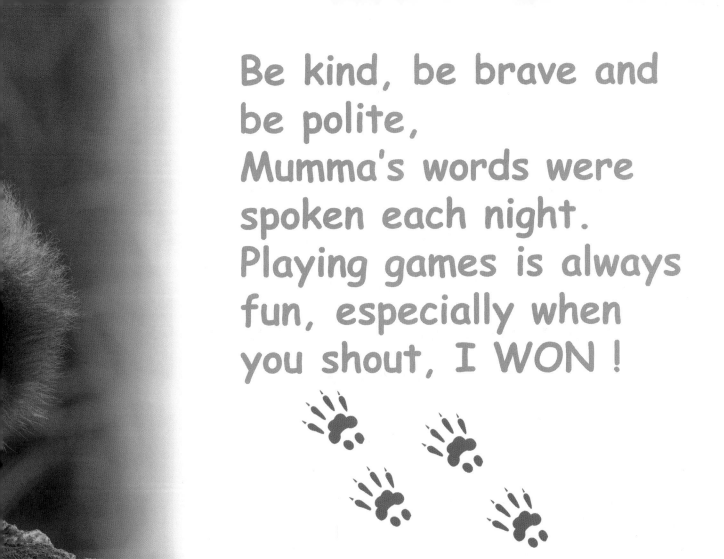

Be kind, be brave and
be polite,
Mumma's words were
spoken each night.
Playing games is always
fun, especially when
you shout, I WON !

Be kind, be brave and
be polite,
Mumma's words were
spoken each night.
Set your imagination
free; explore new things,
she would say to me.

Be kind, be brave and
be polite,
Mumma's words were
spoken each night.
Let's play a game
of hide-and-seek,
but don't forget you
must not PEEK ...

Be kind, be brave and
be polite,
Mumma's words were
spoken each night.
Don't forget your five-
a-day, it helps to
keep the bugs away.

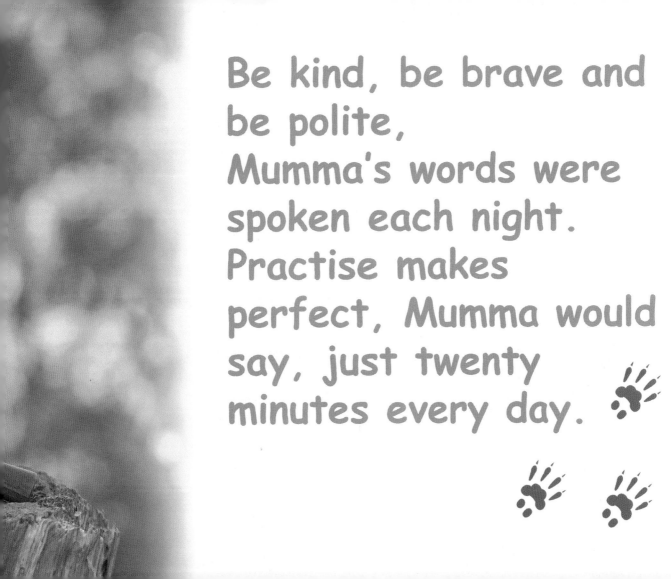

Be kind, be brave and
be polite,
Mumma's words were
spoken each night.
Practise makes
perfect, Mumma would
say, just twenty
minutes every day.

Be kind, be brave
and be polite,
Mumma's words
were spoken each
night.
Magic moments all
around, Ssshhhhh,
don't make a sound.

Be kind, be brave and
be polite,
Mumma's words were
spoken each night.
Sing, dance and play
a merry tune; watch
the stars and say
goodnight to the moon.

Be kind, be brave and
be polite,
Mumma's words were
spoken each night.
Believe in yourself
everyday, be bold be
wise and show the way.

Be kind, be brave and
be polite,
Mumma's words were
spoken each night.
Smiles brighten the
dullest of days, they
make you feel special,
dear Mumma would say.

Be kind, be brave and
be polite,
Mumma's words were
spoken each night.
Always be the one to
share, it truly shows
how much you care ...

Be kind, be brave and be polite,
Mumma's words were spoken each night.
Let's have fun and learn to bake; the end result, delicious cake ...

Be kind, be brave and
be polite,
Mumma's words were
spoken each night.
Creativity is so much
fun, especially when
you're the messy one!

Be kind, be brave and
be polite,
Mumma's words were
spoken each night.
Feel the earth beneath
your feet, nothing else
so pure and sweet.

Printed in Great Britain
by Amazon

86605200R00022